THE OLD MAN'S PRAYER

Quran Stories for Little Hearts

By
SANIYASNAIN KHAN

The Prophet Zakariyya ﷺ was a noble man. He was an uncle of Maryam (Mary), and the priest of the shrine in Jerusalem. When Maryam was given to the service of Allah, the Prophet Zakariyya ﷺ was made Maryam's guardian.

4

Whenever the Prophet Zakariyya ﷺ visited Maryam in her niche (*mihrab*) in the shrine, he would find that she had fresh food.

5

He would be amazed at this and would ask Maryam where this food came from. "This is from Allah," Maryam would answer. "Allah gives in plenty to whoever He pleases."

When the Prophet Zakariyya ﷻ reached old age and was still childless, he prayed to Allah for a son: "My bones are weak and my head is shining with grey hair. Yet, my Lord! I have never been disappointed in praying to You."

Allah heard his beautiful
prayers and said, "Zakariyya! We
bring you good news of a son
whose name will be Yahya".

But Zakariyya  wondered: "My Lord! How shall I have a son when my wife is barren, and I am now very old?"

But Allah said: "So it shall be. It is easy for Me, for
I created you, before which you were nothing."

Zakariyya ﷺ said: "O my Lord! Give me a sign!" Allah said, "Your sign is that you shall not speak to anyone for three nights, though otherwise in good health."

The Prophet Zakariyya ﷺ was filled with joy and words of thanks came pouring from his lips. He came out of the shrine and exhorted his people to praise the Lord morning and evening.

And so in his old age the Prophet Zakariyya's prayers were answered and he had a son whose name was Yahya (John) عليه السلام.

Yahya ﷺ grew up to be a loving soul. Allah gave him wisdom, grace and purity while yet a child and made him a prophet.

20

Yahya ﷺ grew up to be a good man, honouring his father and mother. He neither thought too much of himself nor did he disobey Allah.

This story reminds us that Allah helps the believers in wonderful ways. He hears the prayers of His servants, even if what they want seems impossible.

Find Out More
To know more about the message and meaning of Allah's words, look up the following parts of the Quran which tell the story of the Prophet Zakariyya.
Surah Maryam 19:2-15

عَلَيْهِ السَّلَام *Alayhis Salam* 'May peace be upon him.'
The customary blessings on the prophets.